Y0-BCE-491

A Year to Grow

A Year to Grow

by Felice Holman

Illustrated by

EMILY ARNOLD MC CULLY

W · W · Norton & Company · Inc·

New York

BY FELICE HOLMAN

A Year to Grow

The Cricket Winter

The Blackmail Machine

The Witch on the Corner

Professor Diggins' Dragons

Victoria's Castle

Silently, the Cat, and Miss Theodosia

Elisabeth and the Marsh Mystery

Elisabeth, the Bird Watcher

Elisabeth, the Treasure Hunter

Library of Congress Catalog Card No. 68-27636

Published simultaneously in Canada by
George J. McLeod Limited, Toronto
Printed in the United States of America
1 2 3 4 5 6 7 8 9 0

For

LILA K. PIPER,

a bright light in a dark place,

and for

DOROTHY S. WITHERS,

a friend, indeed

Contents

Contents

I was sent to The Mary Barrows School to "grow up." Exactly how they thought it was going to happen in that chill, dry, gray place, I just don't know.

Chapter 1

Perversely . . . in all the quiet drear of Mary Barrows, something did happen, but it was not in a way that anyone could have foreseen, so they may have no credit for it–not my parents, nor The Mary Barrows School.

Chapter 9

The Preceptress

One

Miss Hill was the preceptress of The Mary Barrows School, a boarding school for young ladies. She was also its nurse. As preceptress, it was her duty to lay down and administer the law. As nurse, it was her job to pick up the pieces. She was an enormous white thing, except for a red face.

Every afternoon at three twenty, the large

Miss Hill sat at a tiny wooden desk near the side door and checked the line of girls going out for the daily walk. *Every girl* went out for either the country walk or the town walk unless she was being disciplined. Sometimes, on a bitter day, it was hard to decide whether to be disciplined or to go out for a walk.

We always used the side door. The front door entering onto the spacious vestibule was

used only twice by the girls of Mary Barrows —the day they arrived at the school and the day they left. Other than that, it was used to receive guests.

At the side door we waited, bundled in dark coats and hats, to be checked by Miss Hill. She found each girl's name on her daily check board, made a mark in the "out" column, and then, if it was a winter day (and it seemed to be winter a good deal of the time), Miss Hill gave a nod, at which the departing girl lifted her green poplin skirt and displayed her legs to the preceptress.

"Miss Hill's chorus line!" Patsy Weeks had whispered in answer to my question the first time I saw this happen. But that wasn't the case at all, of course. Miss Hill was not organizing a chorus line. Miss Hill was checking to see that the student's warm lisle hose and her knitted "woolies" met and overlapped, providing proper warmth, insulation, and modesty.

I got used to the routine of it, as I got used to many other of the Mary Barrows' routines, and after a while it hardly seemed peculiar. I was timid and tried to be inconspicuous, but still I ran afoul of the rules. My own mother got me into some of my first trouble with Miss Hill. My mother was interested in my warmth, too, but she did not understand the precepts of the preceptress.

It was my turn to be checked out one bitter cold day, and I was thinking it was too bad not to have just a light discipline that day. Miss Hill gave me her abrupt nod, which meant pull up the skirt. Then her face seemed to fall all to pieces like a jigsaw puzzle when you joggle it accidentally. The girls around me were laughing, and that infuriated Miss Hill. "Quiet!" she said sharply, "or everyone will have detention after dinner tonight. Everyone! Step out of line." The last was directed at me.

She checked out every one of the girls without another word, and then she turned to me. "Is that your idea of a joke, Julia?"

"No, Miss Hill," I said. "It isn't a joke. They're just woolies, you know."

"They're *red*!" said Miss Hill.

"Yes, Miss Hill. My mother sent them to me." Actually, they were quite gorgeous.

Miss Hill was not intimidated. Her general opinion of motherhood was low. From this rude action alone, she could judge my mother must be unladylike. Ladylikeness was the only real criterion at Mary Barrows. You had it or you didn't. You were or you weren't. Everything else came after that. The whole educational system was focused on the development of a reflex that would carry one with grace, if not distinction, through all life's situations.

Ladies do not whistle. Ladies do not chew gum. I discovered both those things the hard way. I got two weeks of detention in study hall for whistling in the shower room, caught by Miss Hill, herself. For the gum transgression, the standard punishment was for the offender to walk up and down for an hour, from the sundial to the veranda and back, with the gum stuck to one's nose. The best thing was not to chew gum in the winter. I found that out. Apparently ladies did not wear red woolies either.

The rule book at Mary Barrows, it developed, did not provide for discipline in the event of red woolies, but Miss Hill was up to it. The lack of regulations against things did not hamper a person like Miss Hill. That is what preceptresses were for. They were there to perceive and to write precepts against—on the spot, if need be. And she did. The week in study hall got me nicely through the cold snap.

I was fifteen, but shy and unsure. I was sent to The Mary Barrows School to "grow up." Exactly how they thought it was going to happen in that chill, dry, gray place, I just don't know.

Behind my face (the face I kept turned to Miss Hill and the others at Mary Barrows) was where I really lived. I lived there quietly, and if I didn't jounce about too much, some of the awfulness of Mary Barrows hardly touched me.

The Quiet People

Two

The June bugs came long before June and flew unhindered through unscreened windows, throwing their heavy bodies against green walls, diving into us as we studied under desk lamps. I always went to bed before lights-out hour, when the June bugs started, and wrote poetry under the blankets by flashlight. My roommate, Nora, said they didn't bother her, but she was pathologically frightened of everything on earth—living or dead, it didn't matter—and I didn't believe her. I thought she was stuffing the bedclothes in her mouth to keep from screaming when the June bugs threw themselves around in the dark.

We had tried not opening the windows, but the bugs had come anyhow. Perhaps they flew in from the hallway—sometimes they seemed to be coming from the closet—but I said it was spontaneous generation.

I think Nora Williams and I had been matched as roommates because we were both quiet, but I was only quiet on the outside. I had all kinds of things I was thinking and bursting to say. It is just that I hardly ever found anyone to say them to. I did not really believe that Nora had anything to say at all. She was frozen, frightened ice. She said yes, and she said no, and sometimes good night—hardly anything more. This was her seventh year at Mary Barrows, but she had not chosen a roommate from any of the old students. So there we were—two quiet, frightened, slight, abrasive creatures, crammed into a box on the third floor with a scourge of June bugs.

At first Nora seemed just another one of the awful things at Mary Barrows for me, and then, oddly, by and by, she became one of the comforts. You could put words in Nora's mouth and get almost any response you wanted. She was hardly there except to occupy a little space with her body, and yet I was not alone . . . not all alone. When I cried at night, Nora did not ask me why or offer help or comfort. Nora never cried, or at least I never heard her. I thought the cool blue of her eyes and the coldness of her pale skin could not melt into anything like tears. And then, at Christmas she gave me a book of poetry. It was a surprising gift.

When Nora and I went down to dinner in the evening, we walked the whole, long, un-

carpeted third-floor corridor, down
carpeted stairs to the carpeted seco
down the carpeted second flight to t
hall, down the long main hall, across
nex bridge, down the annex stairs,
our separate clubrooms to await th
bell. We never, that I can remembe
word on that walk, nor did our an
of dinner excite hopeful guesses. We
would be a gray slice or lump of s
with mashed potatoes, and gray gr
gray string beans.

Just before and just after supper w
went to our clubrooms. There we
clubs: the V.L.'s, the Y.B.T.'s
R.R.R.'s. The Mary Barrows School had been in existence since years beyond recall, and somewhere back in 1917, or so, someone—perhaps a grateful old graduate—had given an enormous silver loving cup to the school. This elegant trophy was awarded each year to the "best" club and engraved

with its initials. The winning club had the privilege of keeping the cup on its fireplace mantel for the whole following year. The cup was a mass of incriptions: "RRR 1921," "YBT 1922," "RRR 1923," "VL 1924." I can't even guess how "best" was determined in those years, but when I was at Mary Barrows the cup was awarded solely at the mystical whim of the dean, Miss Bertran. What else could it have been? Every girl was assigned arbitrarily to a club at the beginning of the year, and there was only one other function of the clubs besides providing before-and-after-dinner sitting rooms—that was probing the mystery of the club initials. Because it was a fact that over the years the records had been lost, the members scattered, and not one living soul seemed to have even a vague notion of what the club initials stood for. And so we sometimes sat around and guessed; Really Righteous Redheads, Young Beautiful Women, and Virtuous Lasses were some of the more restrained guesses. But no one knew.

That may have been the real obstacle to other club activity. It was hard to get interested in a club whose name and purpose were unknown. All the same, we really did want to win that cup. I can't think why.

We ate our supper at six o'clock. In the early fall and spring it was still light, and the semi-basement room caught the late afternoon sun at an odd angle.

Dean Bertran sat with the preceptress, Miss Hill, at the table closest to the west window. Miss Bertran ate a dinner quite different from ours. Because of frailty, false teeth, and delicate digestion, she ate only young pink lamb chops and young green asparagus or other such delicate foods. The gray dinners never came within the short range of her vision.

The very first punishment I ever received

at Mary Barrows was for speaking at the dinner table. Incredibly, conversation at dinner was forbidden except during the dessert course. The declared reason for this was that the ceiling was low, and under such acoustical conditions, the voices of ninety girls and their teachers would be intolerable for Miss Bertran . . . not to mention, create a very unladylike atmosphere.

Countless evenings, just before our dessert was served and we would start to talk, Miss Bertran would wobble to her fragile feet, assisted by Miss Hill, and, taking her silver spoon in her hand, would tap a few staccato notes on her glass.

Tink, tink, her silver spoon would go against her nice crystal goblet. Then, steadying herself against the table, she would say in a voice, astoundingly strong, "Gulls! Gulls! Gulls! The noise in here is *quite* impossible. I cannot eat another bite." And dramatically pushing away her absolutely clean, bare-boned plate, she would slowly creep out of the sinful, dinful, dining room.

If I ever had been asked to draw a picture of The Mary Barrows School, I would have drawn a hundred girls in dull green uniforms, eating a dull gray supper in a low-ceiled, silent room.

Building a Lady

Three

There were some girls who seemed to get along very well at Mary Barrows. I don't know if they really loved it, but they cried at graduation. I remember that. There was something that made things all right for them and so all wrong for girls like me and Nora. But the girls who really seemed to have fun were the girls who were on the field-hockey teams. They all had a crush on Miss Adams, the gym teacher, and they were always carrying each other everyplace and banging each other on the back. Somehow or other, this was all part of being ladylike, too, and fitted into the Mary Barrows' scheme of things. They always had a lot going on, and sometimes it even looked to me like it might be fun, but mostly it looked awful.

The first day that I went out to play field hockey I was rotten at it. The second day I got kicked in the ankle, and the third day I fell flat on my coccyx bone and was excused for the rest of the season. It was one of my luckiest accidents. The fact that my coccyx bone gave me quite some trouble for a while was a small price to pay for not getting into that hockey costume and beating around the field with a hockey stick, not understanding what in the world I was trying to win and why.

But there were more ways than one to

build the body of a lady, though hockey did seem the accepted way. There was a special thing at Mary Barrows, and Miss Bertran, when she did anything at all, boasted about it. Once a week The Mary Barrows School was visited by Ellen Townley Minor, a short, but plump, middle-aged lady of enormous vitality—the surviving member of a famous theatrical family. First she had a dainty lunch with Miss Bertran, and then she got into a costume based on a pair of ballooning gym bloomers and proceeded to conduct her famous class in the sport—or art (it was hard to tell which)—called "grace." One reason why it was hard to tell was that we got into our hockey suits for this and turned out on the gym floor in sneakers. Then, in long even rows, ninety girls and all physically fit teachers (this ruled out most) went through their weekly alphabet. Alphabet!

Miss Minor put the record on the phonograph, and I kept hoping that just once—

just once—it could have been something other than "*Clair de Lune.*"

"A," called Miss Minor, and her arm rose like a swan's neck over her head, the wrist flicked up; and then *down* came the arm on the downbeat, while Miss Minor bent at her enormous waist and touched her tiny right foot with her plump right hand. A hundred arms followed. Then *up* the same line (having now drawn one side of an enormous "A" in the air). Quickly now, down the other side, reaching over to the left toe. Only halfway back up this time, sweeping limpid arm across to the right to form the crossbar of the "A," graceful hand following leading wrist. And before one drew a breath, "B," boomed Miss Minor, and down she went for the straight line of the "B," back up, two swooping loops—one high, one low—and the "B" was done. "C," she called, rising on the toes of her little right foot and reaching way out to the side with her right arm, as if to pick an irresistible fruit from some high branch.

Then a great sweep back to the left, down to the floor, finishing the "C" with a grand Spencerian flourish. And off to the dramatic "D." By "G" I was always winded, and my coccyx bone gave notice of its recent injury. Several formerly physically fit teachers dropped out by "J." Once a girl fainted executing a "Q" because Miss Minor insisted on starting and finishing the circle at the top, and then diving down to put the little squiggle at the bottom. That was silly. We could have started and finished the circle at the bottom just as well. It did awful things to the blood in one's head the way she did it.

I was always terribly nervous by the time we got to "W." Would "*Clair de Lune*" last? I wanted to rush through "XYZ," just in case. I would much rather have had a few bars of music left over than letters. Would it last? Would it *last*? And it always did. I thought Debussy would have been surprised to know that he wrote a composition just twenty-six letters long.

Nora

Four

My roommate, Nora Williams, was the smartest girl in the school. She was, at any rate, the best student. All her grades were in the nineties, and every month, when the grades were posted, Nora's name always topped the list in every single subject, except gym and music. She never played hard enough in hockey, and Miss Adams was always yelling at her, "Run, Nora. What are you waiting for? Nora, it's yours! Get in there!" And Nora would respond in slow motion, and drive Miss Adams into a fit of disgust and frustration.

In choir Nora opened her mouth, but no sound came out. It always looked as if she were singing, but, as a matter of fact, she wasn't. Miss Goldy would start at the front of the room, waving her little baton, and then move about among the singers, putting her ear close to one and then another to see who was flat. Nearly everyone was. When she came to Nora she would stop and listen, and listen again, look worried (fearing, perhaps, that she'd gone deaf), and then, when she was fairly well convinced that there was no sound coming from Nora's mouth, she would start moving her hands in the air right in front of Nora's face as if pulling a long rope out of her throat, and with it some sound. But Nora would just fix her eyes on the wall behind Miss Goldy and keep forming soundless words with her mouth; and Miss Goldy

would move on, rather puzzled, feeling that, after all, there was some mistake. But Nora's grade always showed the effect of Miss Goldy's doubts.

Nora's absolutely strongest point was Latin, and it was only in this class that she spoke out. She would read endlessly in Latin, if allowed, and Mr. Law was usually quite happy to let her read because he didn't have to correct a word. She was that good. He didn't even have to listen, but could start dreaming —maybe about getting the tulip bulbs in, or mulching the roses, or something. He had, after all, been through *Caesar's Gallic Wars* and *Cicero* for forty years or more, and they may have lost some impact. Nora seemed nearly happy in Latin. It was another world, another time, another language, having nothing whatever to do with right now . . . and right now was all wrong for Nora.

Mr. Law was very pleased with her. "You'll win the Latin prize," he told her one day after the first-quarter grades were in. Nora didn't say anything, but right after that she stopped reading in class, and if Mr. Law asked her a question she gave the wrong answer. Her work went down to a B, and Mary Ellen Popper, who was second best, got to be first best, and Nora wasn't even close. Mary Ellen was pretty sure of herself. Her roommate said she was practicing her acceptance speech before the mirror. Awards day was a big thing. Winning the Latin prize really put you in the limelight.

It was unlike me, but I attacked Nora one evening. I had come from detention in study hall, and she was reading Latin out loud to herself in our room. She was embarrassed and put the book right down and started her algebra.

"Nora," I said. "What are you up to?" It was a more personal question than I had ever put to her—something directed right at her, by name.

"I don't know what you mean," she said in her dead, quiet voice, and she kept her eyes on a spot on the floor somewhere between us both.

"Yes you do." Now I was sorry I had started it. I was not used to challenging people, but I stuck to it. "You're not doing your Latin. Why?"

"Yes, I'm doing my Latin." It was a simple statement. No heat.

"But you're not reciting in class. You're letting Mary Ellen get way ahead of you."

"It doesn't matter."

"But it does matter. You won't get the Latin prize."

Nora almost looked at me, then, but not quite. She never met your eyes, really, but you could see that the expression was the same one that was there when Miss Adams yelled, "It's yours, Nora. Take it. Run!"

Nora was a half-orphan. Her mother had died when she was eight. One of the teachers, Mrs. Lindstrom, told me about it after midyear's. It was an automobile accident. Her father had been driving, but he had only got some broken bones, and Nora was just scratched. He sent her to Mary Barrows then. Nora never mentioned her father—not once—but she used to write to him, and sometimes, but not often, he wrote to her. He was a research scientist at one of the big universities . . . some sort of genius, Mrs. Lindstrom said . . . almost famous.

Dr. Williams came to see Nora twice or three times during the school year. On holidays she stayed at the school. Besides Miss Hill, Miss Bertran, Dr. Duncan and his family, and a few of the staff, there was only one other person that stayed during vacations—a girl whose parents were missionaries in the Congo. You could understand that she had to stay, but I thought Nora must hate her father.

When Nora's father was coming, she was especially quiet and tense for days. She was always terribly neat, though she never seemed to be paying much attention to it. But when her father was expected she spent extra long getting dressed and brushing her hair and filing her nails. Her cold eyes seemed almost hot when she was waiting to be called on a Sunday that he was coming to visit. He didn't take her out to dinner or to the movies or for a drive like most of our parents did. He would talk with her in the lounge or walk with her about the neat paths of the school grounds.

He stayed only an hour or so, and when he left, she would come up to the room and take a book and lie on her bed and pretend to read. By then I had got to know Nora a bit, and in her absolutely dry-eyed way, I felt Nora was weeping. It all happened inside of her. It never showed. She never moved. I wanted to say something. I really wanted to. But I didn't. What could I say?

The second time I saw Nora come back from a visit with her father I felt strongly that I was going to run downstairs and catch Dr. Williams and say, "Take her away with you;

why don't you?" I wanted to kick him, and yell at him, and say, "Why do you keep her here, you silly, stupid man! I thought you were some kind of genius!"

But I had seen him waiting in the vestibule for Nora to come down, and he looked like broken branches from rotting trees—an old ghost of a man. I could not yell at a broken branch. I could not yell at anything, then, unless it could not be heard.

Doctor Duncan and the Sinners

Five

The staff of Mary Barrows—the hierarchy—went like this. Dr. Duncan was president, Miss Bertran, dean, and Miss Hill, preceptress. Dr. Duncan was a Doctor of Divinity, and his congregation was the ninety girls of Mary Barrows who met at nine o'clock each morning in the "chapel"—a grand name for a room more properly called a room—and at vespers each Sunday, held in the seeming luxury of the carpeted lounge. Dr. Duncan was tall and rugged–rigid was more true–and everyone was afraid of him. He had our sympathy only because he bore a heavy burden. His only son, Jimmy, who lived on the school grounds with his nurse, was a mental defective. He was the object of much talk.

Dr. Duncan distracted us all terribly by shifting about on his feet while he prayed. I kept thinking there must be a hot pipe in the floor under Dr. Duncan, and after a while it got uncomfortable just to watch him. During vespers I used to stare at the ornate pattern of the enormous oriental rug in the lounge to keep my mind off Dr. Duncan's discomforts.

There was no getting away from the fact that Dr. Duncan saw us all as ninety sinners, near-sinners, or potential sinners. The chapel was dark, varnished, dreary with school desks. It doubled as the study hall and detention hall. In morning chapel, Dr. Duncan stood on a little podium at a kind of pulpit, and everything was more impersonal—a few quick readings and responses, a verse of a hymn, a hasty benediction. At vespers it was different . . . close. We crowded into the lounge, and there weren't enough chairs so some of us sat on the carpet. Dean Bertran would take her stand at the west window, steadying herself on the sill, and the late afternoon light silhouetted her bones through the sheer voile dress. Miss Bertran was made mostly of papier mâché. (She had an open fireplace in her room, and her terrible dryness worried me—she was the most flammable thing in the school.) She nearly didn't exist, anyhow, except as a power. You could see clearly, as she stood against the window at vespers, that she was only a profile.

Dr. Duncan said "Let us pray," as though he were speaking to a slowpoke child, saying, "Come along, Milly." And though he closed his eyes and his voice was strong, I was not truly convinced that I was a sinner. I knew I was terribly imperfect, but my imperfections did not seem to me to be in the way of transgressions, but of lacks.

But when Dr. Duncan talked of "love" I listened, because more than anything I wanted to be loved, more than being first in the class or even more than writing the greatest poem that had ever been written. My parents loved me. I knew that. They loved me a great deal, and they thought I was wonderful. They said so. But the thing is, *I* knew I wasn't. I knew it strongly, and it made it hard to bear that kind of love. It made me feel cold instead of warm. Even so, I would start to like people, and then, if they came toward me, I was afraid they would see my imperfections, and I was afraid of what they would expect of me . . . and I pulled back. But when I listened to Dr. Duncan and what he said about love—God's love of man, man's love of God—it didn't seem to have to do with my real life any more than the sin did.

When he spoke of sin, I wasn't even sure

what he was talking about. I knew I didn't steal or even cheat on examinations, and I didn't lie very much. And if he spoke of sin too long, I would go behind my face, and in the afternoon light Dr. Duncan used to turn a sort of yellow-green. And then I would take my eyes from his shifting feet to the Oriental carpet and stare and stare, and the patterns would move and squirm, and sometimes one would turn into a snake and start to coil its way around the intricate designs, coiling and uncoiling on its way across the carpet to me. And then, before it got to me, Dr. Duncan would have us all rise and sing the final hymn.

But one Sunday just before the Christmas holiday, Dr. Duncan made his sermon quite a bit longer, and as he got more and more uncomfortable on his feet, the snake started to move faster, and before we got to the hymn the snake reached me. A sound came out of my throat and I put my hands over my face.

And then I knew everyone was looking at me, and I started to cough. I coughed and coughed, and Miss Hill led me out of the room.

After that, and for quite a while, I began to think that perhaps, after all, I was a sinner.

Mental Hygiene

Six

The teachers at The Mary Barrows School were culled for qualities that were imponderable. They were nearly all ladies and lived at the school; they had that in common. But there was also old Mr. Law, who taught Latin. He lived in a big house down the road from the school and came in three times a week to hold classes. The rest of the time he gardened, except in the winter when we all believed he simply froze up. And there was Mr. Gervais, who was quite young, probably. He taught civics, and he lived with his mother on the other side of the village.

Miss Bolt taught art, and I was almost convinced she was color blind. Either that or she just didn't know the names of the colors. It had to be one of those things.

"The purple is too deep," she would say of the orange. The other agonizing thing she did was to actually grab your hand holding the pencil and guide it as she felt the line should go. She was not above making changes on a finished piece of art, making the bowl more symmetrical or perfecting the shape of a petal. She put clouds in a landscape I painted.

English history was a slow procession of kings, queens, and dates, all in black and white. The Hundred Years' War lasted for eons, and Henrys, Edwards, and Richards slowly merged into one multicrowned, stooped monarch.

Miss Allen, a fortyish spinster, taught us English history. She was actually a fairly attractive blonde lady who looked as if there were still life, but she presented a class of unvarying tedium. The most incredible thing about English history was that Patsy Weeks knew as a fact that Miss Allen was engaged to be married . . . had been for five years. Speculating on the probability of this occurrence lent whatever interest there was to that hour for me.

Then, there was Mrs. Lindstrom. She came in the second term to replace the ailing Miss Barnes as teacher of mental hygiene. She was an oddity at Mary Barrows. In the first place, she had been married and her husband was dead. She had a child of ten, now in the school. They had both come that year from Hong Kong, where Mrs. Lindstrom had been headmistress of an English school. There was something romantic sounding about the whole thing.

The curriculum of mental hygiene changed sharply with the arrival of Mrs. Lindstrom, and for three months, until Dr. Duncan stepped in, it was the most interesting subject in the school. It became a course about everything. The most fascinating books from Mrs. Lindstrom's private library—a much-traveled packing case—sped from hand to hand. Then, disregarding the textbook issued by Mary Barrows, Mrs. Lindstrom turned the class discussions to personal problems—all kinds of things that were on our minds. At first everyone was backward about speaking out in class, but before long, we were all eager to bring up a subject that worried us. Some of the girls had very interesting worries. Patsy Weeks, who looked healthy and normal as anything, said her mother had a liver condition, and Patsy was afraid she would have it, too. Then we talked about what kinds of things were inherited. That's the way subjects came up. The thing we found out was that almost every girl had something on her mind or in the back of her mind that she wanted to talk to someone about.

Each of us was scheduled for a private weekly conference with Mrs. Lindstrom, a routine that had not been in the mental hygiene curriculum before. In these talks we might start to talk about a book we were reading, but then we would turn to talk about our most private feelings. I started by showing Mrs. Lindstrom my poetry; there was nobody else at Mary Barrows I would show it to. They said things about myself that I could not say any other way. But then, after a while, I found myself telling her things I felt about people, loneliness, love. I even told her how I never felt as if I were a real person at all. One of my poems told her that, anyway, " . . . an odd guest" it went, "treading the edges of the real world . . . a transient."

"I feel," I told her, "that all of time is *now*, and now seems so useless." I had never been able to say anything like that to anyone before . . . only write it.

"There is a high dam," I told her once, trying to explain how I felt toward people, "between me and everyone else."

She would look very closely at me when I spoke, as if she were very interested, and there would be some laughter in her eyes—but not derisive—that said it was not *all* bad.

"Sometime—any time at all—*something* will happen (some little thing, perhaps) that will change the way you feel just enough . . . just enough to break the dam, Julie," Mrs. Lindstrom said to me. I thought about it a great deal, and after that I found I was waiting for "the something." It was a kind of hopeful feeling.

My roommate, Nora, became extraordinarily attached to Mrs. Lindstrom. Nora would lurk outside her door, waiting for an extra chance to speak to her. She became sullen, sometimes, and jealous if Mrs. Lindstrom gave me an extra few minutes. But after Nora had been talking with Mrs. Lindstrom for a

few weeks, Nora started to talk to me now and then. Quite contrary to my notion that she had nothing to say, it seemed she really had a great deal to say, but no way to say it—a great slough of feeling, but no way to show it. The words never did come freely, nor the feeling, either, but gradually I began to feel that Nora was a strange . . . an unsteady friend . . . but a friend.

One day Dr. Duncan came to the mental hygiene class very purposefully. He strode in and sat in the back, and Mrs. Lindstrom just went on talking. Someone had said something about hating something or other—a food, maybe—and Mrs. Lindstrom had said that was a strong feeling, and then we started to talk about hating things. Dr. Duncan got up and started to walk up and down between the desks in the class. It was distracting. He would reach over and turn over a book on a girl's desk and move on. I had nothing but my Latin book and a notebook. Nora had her algebra book. It didn't cross my mind, then,

that he could be looking for the mental hygiene textbooks. He walked up to the front, while Mrs. Lindstrom talked on, and looked at the books on her desk. Then he walked out.

The next day Dr. Duncan fired Mrs. Lindstrom and took over the mental hygiene course himself. She called us all to say goodby. She said only that she and Dr. Duncan had different ideas about the subject. They certainly did. It became quite another course after that.

I was terribly lonely without Mrs. Lindstrom. I had grown to look forward to my visits with her more than I had realized. I felt even sadder for Nora. She was alone again. I knew a special thing about her because I knew it about myself. Before Mrs. Lindstrom came, in different ways, we both, Nora and I, had been touching people only at the edges of their lives with the edges of our lives.

Miss Allen's Assignation

Seven

Miss Allen's fiancé was coming from Michigan to see her. That's the news Patsy Weeks had for us, and it caused a lot of talk around the English-history class. Patsy Weeks was right in the center of it because she was close to Miss Allen. It was like this: he was not *exactly* coming to see her, but he was a businessman in Battle Creek and he was going to New York for a convention, and she was going to New York to meet him. Patsy had seen his snapshot on Miss Allen's bureau. He was simply marvelous. She was going to borrow it to show us as soon as she could. The thing I liked was the word "meet." To "meet" him was somehow a very special, intimate thing—an assignation.

When Miss Allen, herself, would gaze out of the window during English history, you could think she had probably been a pretty sort of young girl. It wasn't even that she was not pretty now; she just had no texture at all . . . vague, like a watercolor painting without the benefit of Miss Bolt filling in the detail. After she had left a room, you were never really sure that she had been there in the first place.

I looked closely at the snapshot of Mr. White when Patsy finally produced it. Mr. White was his name, and that's what Patsy always called him. I kept imagining that Miss

Allen would say to him in their tenderest moment, "I love and respect you, Mr. White," and he would say to her, "Likewise, Miss Allen."

The snapshot of Mr. White was as vague as the real Miss Allen. He seemed to be in some sort of uniform, but whether it was an army uniform, or a band uniform, or a policeman's or fireman's uniform, or a costume from *Yeoman of the Guard* was hard to tell because of the fuzziness of the picture. He had light or light-struck hair, and a light-struck face, and thin-rimmed glasses. The expression was of one taken by surprise.

Patsy Weeks got more and more excited about Miss Allen's trip. "I'm going to lend her my cosmetic case," she said. "It's fitted. It's got lots of places to keep all kinds of things, and a special compartment for aspirin, and cotton, and iodine."

To Patsy, a place for aspirin, iodine, cotton, and adhesive bandages was as essential as a place for money in a pocketbook. Patsy had two favorite haunts at Mary Barrows; one was Miss Allen's room, where she learned all about Mr. White and then retold the saga to anyone who would listen. The other place was the infirmary, where she reported nearly every morning to get a couple of aspirin, or have her temperature taken, or have an adhesive bandage put on a new scrape or cut. She did get more than her share of scrapes because she was rather clumsy and rushed about so much that she took a lot of tumbles.

But she was an exceptionally cheerful girl, and once she got going in the morning and was sure she did not have a temperature and that her newest cut was going to stop bleeding, she was fine and stayed fine until the next morning. Considering her dependence on the infirmary, I didn't see how she had the nerve to badger Miss Hill the way she did. But she did. She was the prime perpetrator of Miss Hill's harassment. Once, on an especially dull evening, she got twenty-five girls to go and stand outside the infirmary after dinner to complain of stomach-ache. During that whole night, Miss Hill was running around looking at girls and turning out the kitchen, suspecting food poisoning and being scared to death of some sort of scandal.

Patsy had double-jointed knees and elbows, and she used to jar Miss Hill every single time Miss Hill saw her stumble. Patsy would lie on the ground with an elbow at some impossible angle, or her knees bent up absolutely double beneath her. As many times as Miss Hill had seen Patsy fall, she could never believe something wasn't really broken. But everything on Patsy was flexible. She could spend half an evening on her bed with her legs clear around her neck, and read. She said it hurt her back a little, but she did it anyway. Patsy's mother sent her boxes of food every week, and unlike the other boxes that mothers sent, it never had a single sweet in it. It had fresh carrots.

It had cookies made of carrots. It had candies made out of carrots. And it had boxes of dried prunes. Patsy ate them all with pleasure, and nobody ever raided her food box. More than that, Patsy was possibly the only girl at Mary Barrows who thought the food in the dining hall was just fine. She always cleaned up her whole plate and enjoyed it.

There was something special that I liked about her. Except for her aspirins, she seemed so real and sort of simple and straight, but the most appealing thing to me was that she was never sarcastic or really mean. That was something that kept chilling me over and over at Mary Barrows—the disdain and meanness that got into the voices of the girls. Sometimes I thought it might be part of being sophisticated, but if I used that tone myself, when I was feeling especially sour, it never sounded sophisticated and it felt bad right away. I thought I could really like Patsy very much. I sat around often and listened to her tell all about Miss Allen—every word. She liked that, I think.

"She's making a new dress," Patsy said, giving the latest news. "It's a flowered sheer. It'll be very chic and springish under a winter coat. She's going to wear her navy coat, and navy shoes, and carry a red bag, which will pick up the roses in the flowered print. She's going to be devastating!" Patsy looked so pleased.

I looked straight at Miss Allen for the whole history lesson that day and tried to imagine her devastating, waiting in a hotel lobby for Mr. White to come down . . . leaning against the pillar of the lobby . . . no, probably seated in a leather chair . . . very *soignée* . . . and devastating. But the fact is, I could not manage it. Miss Allen was hunched over the desk most of the hour, and she had a deep frown on her brow and a fairly discontented look. I transferred her to the lobby just like that, and no matter how I dressed up the lobby with crystal chandeliers and bellboys with gold braid, Miss Allen did not look devastating or soignée or happy. She just kept sitting uncomfortably in the lobby chair, leaning forward, frowning, and looking nervously about for Mr. White. The time kept going by, going by, going by, and she kept watching the indicator of the elevator—but no Mr. White. I was really disappointed. What I wanted was for her to rise slowly and very elegantly, when she saw him, and move gracefully across the lobby to meet his extended hands with hers. They would press their hands warmly together—nothing more—but it was a mature gesture of deep affection and respect.

As the days went by, Patsy brought whatever news she picked up, though it generally added up to the same thing. I listened attentively without asking any questions, and each day I kept reconstructing Miss Allen in that lobby chair, and each day Mr. White did not come. I was getting a little nervous about it. Then I tried moving her out of the chair, going to the desk to inquire; and the hotel clerk would just shrug.

"Just when *is* the trip?" I finally got myself to ask Patsy because I really wanted to get it over with.

"In two weeks," breathed Patsy, happy to be the source of all knowledge about the most exciting thing going on.

It was still too long, and I tried to take my mind off it and tried to think about the Hundred Years' War, which was still going on. I felt that war was going to have to stop if we were ever going to get through English history that year. Then, finally, I had to try moving Miss Allen out of the hotel lobby entirely. I put her in a little restaurant—very intimate and charming. She was led to a small table by a very gracious proprietor who flicked off the tablecloth and asked her if she would have an *apéritif*. She said she would wait for her escort. Behind her back, the proprietor and the waiter exchanged knowing glances. And then, it started happening again! She waited, and she waited, and waited, and after a while, she knew he was not coming.

I saw Patsy after breakfast the next morning. I was going to the infirmary myself, for chapped lips. I wanted to say, "I'll walk you to the infirmary," but I never said things like that. I waited for other people to say them. How could I know if they would want me to walk with them? But Patsy didn't ask me; in fact, she turned off into the wrong corridor—the way to her room. In spite of myself, I called, "Patsy, you're going the wrong way." I laughed. "Don't you know the way to the infirmary?"

"I'm not going to the infirmary," Patsy said. "I'm sick," and she put her hands over her face.

"But if you're sick . . . come on, Patsy, I'll take you." Sometimes I surprised myself those days.

"No!" she said. "I don't want to. Oh, Julie, why did it have to happen to *her*? Why?"

"What is it? What's the matter?" I was concerned at her distress, but at the same time enchanted by her actually entreating me that way.

Patsy was sobbing hard now. "She's not going. She's not going on the trip. Miss Allen's not going. She isn't going to New York!"

"After all that?" was what I said. "But why?"

"He isn't coming, that's all. He just isn't coming."

"Why not?"

"She doesn't know. He just isn't coming. It'll kill her . . . just kill her." I took Patsy to her room then, an arm around her shoulders. It was a good friendly feeling, in spite of Patsy's grief. And then something started to nag me.

I was very uneasy next morning. I watched Miss Allen all during the history class. She looked absolutely the same—vague, textureless, hunched over the book, going on and on about the Hundred Years' War. But still the thing was nagging me, and I saw her again on the leather chair in the lobby and Mr. White never appearing. And I asked myself over and over, "Is it possible? Could I have jinxed them with my daydreams? Could *I* have made it happen? Could *anyone* make it happen? I wished that Mrs. Lindstrom were there and I could ask her. I felt so terribly, terribly sinful that I could hardly bear it. I looked about to see if anyone could notice that I was sinful, and then I saw Patsy. She looked ever so much more grieved and distressed than Miss Allen, and suddenly I had what seemed a hopeful idea . . . a way out for myself.

"Patsy," I whispered, "are you sure there really *is* a Mr. White? Are you *sure*?"

Patsy did not answer, but she looked at me with such terrible anger, and fury, and hate that I knew, without surprise, that I had lost another friend before she had even really become one.

And then I started to love Mr. Gervais.

The Love of Mr. Gervais

Eight

The truth is I did not love Mr. Gervais at the beginning of the school year. I didn't even like him. I didn't like civics one bit, so I didn't do well in civics, and Mr. Gervais didn't regard me very highly, and so I didn't like Mr. Gervais. I did not even think Mr. Gervais was nice looking. He had thin dark hair, and thin dark suits, and a sort of thin dark walk. He had pale, pale skin. Everyone knew he lived with his mother, and they thought he was a kind of sissy.

Death transformed Mr. Gervais—his mother's death. He was not in school for many days afterwards. Old Miss Bolt sat at his desk and gave us busywork. When Mr. Gervais finally came back, the change in him was so clear to me! I could see how hurt he was . . . how alone. Then I started to love him.

When I went on the afternoon walk to town, sometimes I could see Mr. Gervais walking ahead of me to the four-family house where he had lived with his mother and now lived alone. Sometimes, as I was passing the building, he would be standing in the little vestibule with its four brass letter boxes and four black bells, looking at the mail. Or he might just be opening the door with his key. There was no one in the apartment now to open the vestibule door from within by pushing the buzzer in the apartment. No one to welcome him.

How unbearably pathetic he was! His thinness now really seemed nice and sort of attractive. His thin dark hair was rather childlike. His pale skin made him look sensitive. At first I wanted so much to tell him that I was alone, too. But presently, I wanted to tell him that he was not alone—that I was there.

Suddenly I started to do better in civics. Perhaps it was the only thing that I could do for him. I studied every lesson because, while I was studying civics, I was thinking of Mr. Gervais. Sometimes I would wait after class, and when he was through talking to anyone else who had stayed after class, I would say, "Would you please be kind enough to explain about apportionment because I really didn't understand all that about apportionment." And I would hold the book, pointing to the place that confused me . . . hold the book close to his face, almost like a touch. And my hand was sometimes quivery.

Mr. Gervais wore heavy glasses, and he would peer and squint through them to the

place I indicated in the book, and patiently explain about apportionment, or whatever it was that day. And sometimes he would look up at me, and it seemed to me his look was probing and meaningful, although sometimes I feared it was just the way his poor eyes looked. And I would watch to see if he looked at the other girls that way. Sometimes I thought he did, but sometimes I was sure he did not.

I looked forward to reciting in class. It was like a private conversation with Mr. Gervais.

" 'Judgment in cases of impeachment shall not extend further than to removal from office,' " I would begin, " 'and disqualification to hold and enjoy any office of honor, trust or profit under the United States; but the party convicted . . .' " and he would say, "Absolutely correct." And I would treasure the words "Absolutely correct," and mull them over when I was back in my room, and think that there might have been something in the way he said them . . . or even that "absolutely correct" could mean several things, actually.

After that I always chose the town walk in the afternoon, hoping to see Mr. Gervais. Nora, as usual, accompanied me, silent and sometimes a step or two in back of me. When I caught sight of him I would follow him—oh, way back, a half-block or more—and pretend we were walking together. I felt I could project my companionship across that length of pavement. He walked without looking around, his head down, watching where he put his feet. Sometimes he stopped at the small grocery shop and bought a bag of vegetables or a loaf of bread. When he did that, I would stop and look at the things in the window of the stationery store. After a while I knew every single item in that window. I could have made a list of them with my eyes closed. When he came out of the grocery with the little brown paper bag, I couldn't help imagining the lonely supper, prepared in his tiny kitchen, and eaten while he marked the civics papers. Sometimes I thought I could see spots on the papers which supported this idea. I loved the spots.

And that is when I began to get the very strong notion of fixing his supper for him. Why not! Not every night, of course. It would be too hard to sneak out on a regular basis. But several of the older girls did sneak out to smoke after supper. They used to climb out the annex lavatory window. Everybody knew it. I really didn't know how to cook, but that was not the immediate problem. It didn't even matter. In my plan, I never sat and ate

with him, but I came and set the table attractively while the chops cooked. I always put fresh flowers on the table—winter or summer—and made a fresh tossed salad. And while he ate, I just sat quietly by. Then, while he marked papers, I did up the dishes, straightened up a bit, and brushed his coat. We didn't talk much, but the sense of companionship grew until we both felt warm and protected. Then, when it was time to go, I left without disturbing him, ran back to the school, and climbed in the window of the annex lavatory. It was a wonderful plan.

During my love for Mr. Gervais the days at Mary Barrows were almost bearable. Life felt bigger . . . not so tight. I felt that this must be "the something" that Mrs. Lindstrom had meant.

One day, I was one of the last girls checked out, and I got a late start on my walk. I hurried at a real run, leaving Nora behind, but Mr. Gervais was way ahead of me and I only glimpsed him coming out of the grocery store. By the time I had reached the four-family house, he had already checked his mail box, opened the door, and disappeared. I looked up the street; Nora was stopping at the post office. We were *never* supposed to leave our walking partners, but I grew bold and stepped into the vestibule. I looked at the mail boxes. The name card on his box still read "Mrs. G.L. Gervais, Mr. R.E. Gervais." It made me ache all the more. Under each box was a black bell button. If you were to ring it, the occupant of the apartment would push an answering buzzer in his own hallway and release the vestibule door lock. He's there, I thought. Right now! He's up there. I could ring the bell, and he would let me in. I held my finger over the bell button. Then I turned and went out onto the street and picked up Nora as she was coming out of the post office. I felt wonderful. I went back to school and spent an hour memorizing Article Five of the Constitution of the United States, and I knew that Mr. Gervais' mind and my mind were turning on the very same thing. It was a very nice communication.

I don't know what would have happened if Mr. Gervais had not asked me to come and see him after classes one day. *He asked me to stay after classes*! I almost couldn't stand the wait all day. The suspense was unbearable. Unbearable! I got a demerit in English history for not hearing a question. I sat in an algebra class for ten minutes before I realized I was not in my Latin class. I was late for Latin and got another demerit. It didn't matter. All that mattered was that Mr. Gervais was waiting for me. Mr. Gervais was waiting for *me*!

There were three other girls in his classroom when I got there at the end of the day. Two more came in while I waited, but I let them go ahead of me. When they had all gone, I walked up to the desk and just stood there, not looking at him. I don't know if he was looking at me, but I heard him say, "I'm giving you an 'A' for this marking period, Julia. I like to make a point of complimenting a student who makes such obvious progress. You're doing very good work this semester. Very good work." And then I looked at him, and he looked at me, too, and in that moment, in that look, I felt I could hear him say, "*Oh, please come and fix my supper, if only now and then. . . .*" *And I said*, "*Yes, I will.*" And then he said, aloud, "Thank you for coming by." That was all. That was all!

I knew what to do, now. I rushed up to my room for my coat and hat, but I took a long time, putting them on carefully, and I got the shoe brush and brushed my shoes. I looked around for my new gloves. I managed to be the last girl checked out. Nora was waiting on the veranda.

"Let's stop at the library," I said. At the

library I went up the steps ahead of her and out the side door onto the street. Then I rushed down the street to Mr. Gervais' house and into the hallowed vestibule. I was out of breath and my knees were shaking. Now, my hand was shaking as I brushed it over the nameplate, "Mr. R.E. Gervais," and let it come to rest directly over the bell. I thought, "I shall do it. I shall do it!" And with a kind of spasm of the finger, I pushed the little black button.

Then I became paralyzed. My finger recoiled from the bell and became painful . . . truly painful. My lips hurt where I must have been biting them. I closed my eyes.

And then the clatter of the buzzer began—the clatter I had heard in my imagination so many times—*Mr. Gervais reaching out to me, saying, "Come."* The buzzer clattered again.

A mythical creature released from a spell, I came to life and ran. I ran and ran, past the library, with the waiting Nora on its

steps, past the post office, the grocery, the stationery store, up the road to The Mary Barrows School, up the two flights to my room, and closed the door.

And I wept then, because I knew that this was *not* "the something."

The Something

Nine

There were the usual bouquets of school horrors and rumors to liven some days—a girl caught stealing, two girls caught smoking, a teacher said to be "secretly married." The girl who was caught stealing was caught in a highly dramatic way. Things had been missing—money mostly. Small amounts. The girl was caught by some cash being "planted" in a bureau that had been robbed before. It was sprinkled with a powder that stained the hands green and could not be washed off. *Voilà*! The girl with the green hands at dinner that night was the thief! It was too bad—really awful—but it did spice things up a bit.

The most persistent and intriguing talk centered about the presence in the school of Jimmy Duncan, the president's son. The stories about him were varied and unreliable, but it was definitely known that he was abnormal in some way—retarded, mentally defective. Mrs. Lindstrom had told us he was Mongoloid. (Perhaps that helped to get her fired.) She said he was probably about twenty-one, but he looked like an oversized anomalous child from the distance, as we usually saw him. He should be dead by now, one of the girls said. She knew about such people. They didn't live long.

After my love for Mr. Gervais, I seldom

took the town walk in the afternoon. I took the country walk whenever I could. I was writing a lot of poetry then, and the really lovely countryside gave me the feeling, even walking in a group, of total loneliness, and loneliness was my best subject. Walking along the road, bordered by winter snow or sered winter grasses, I experienced insight into my loneliness. I felt that Nora was a friend, but it was so lopsided. There was nothing warming in it. For a while I had thought Patsy was the sort of friend I would like, but Patsy turned on me. Patsy didn't need me. Mr. Gervais! That name still embarrassed me. I never looked at him in civics anymore. Never. Mrs. Lindstrom was wonderful, but Mrs. Lindstrom was gone. And so, as I walked on the country road, I laved myself heavily in my loneliness and it seemed my only true and complete experience. Sometimes I felt as though loneliness were love.

And then another fortunate accident happened—I tripped one day when I was out walking. It was the beginning of something.

It was early in the spring, when the snow had melted but the new grass had not yet grown. I was scuffling along, thinking about a poem, when I stumbled on a loose stone, turned my ankle, and fell. The girls marched right along ahead, the gym teacher in the lead with her coterie vying for her arm. The stragglers whispered in twos and threes. Not one of them seemed to notice that I had fallen, and with sudden resentment, I decided to stay where I was until they returned. The pain in my ankle passed quickly, but it seemed a very good excuse.

When the walkers were well out of sight, I decided to take a look about. I stepped off the road, limped up the incline into an enormous meadow spreading like a plain until it came to the foot of a distant hill. But not a hundred yards from me, right out in the middle of nothing, was an iron rail fence marking off a small square area. I would not have been more surprised to see the Persian rug from the lounge. It seemed so oddly useless and incongruous–out of context–in that great dry empty meadow. Suddenly, I became reckless and, forgetting the sore ankle, I ran across the field, stumbling over withered grasses tangled on what seemed to be an old road. As I ran, I could see an open gate on one side of the railing. Perhaps there had been a house there at one time, I thought. Perhaps it had burned down, leaving the fence as a monument.

Just before I reached the gate, I saw the first gray stone above the weeds and grasses, then another and another, leaning at odd angles, fallen, broken, but unmistakably gravestones.

I slowed to a walk and very hesitantly went through the gate. I was trembling from such hard running, but perhaps, too, from pure excitement. I had run away from the group!

I had made an extraordinary discovery! I looked at the stone nearest the gate. The carving was so eroded that I couldn't read it. But the next stone was dated 1809, and the next 1803, and as I walked around and bent and peered, I found that every stone I could read was dated in the early eighteen hundreds. In

one corner, I found six stones with the same family name—all children who had died within a few months of each other! Then, suddenly, in the middle of that field, I cried. I cried hard, for the six children lying beneath the weedy earth, for all those tiny New England souls that never grew up. And I think I cried, too, for my own restless soul, which was trying so hard to find a way to grow beneath the stiff green poplin.

I walked about and walked about, and lost track of time. I ran my hand all around the four sides of the railing. Some of it was leaning, but most of it was standing quite strong. Perhaps it was not as old as the stones. I looked around at everything carefully, feeling I was looking for something. I hated to leave, but finally the problem of joining the walkers began to press itself upon me. I tugged at the old gate and tried to close it behind me, but it had grown into the earth and I couldn't move it. Then I ran across the field toward the road.

The athletic vanguard of the walking group was just appearing around the bend, and it turned out to be a simple thing to fall in behind them. I waited for someone to say something, but no one did. I had not been missed because no one knew I was there in the first place.

Then life took on real color for me at Mary Barrows. The routines were the same. The classes were as dreary as ever, the food as gray, but my afternoons were brilliant with purpose.

Every afternoon I dropped casually behind the stragglers on the country walk. I became very skillful at this. I found a safer place a little farther up the road, where a tall privet hedge allowed me to step out of sight in one quick motion. It was absolutely foolproof. No one ever saw me leave the road. The nearest I ever came to being discovered was when a straggler saw me step back into line one day.

"Whatever were you doing behind that hedge?" she asked, but without much real interest.

"Just straightening my stocking," I lied, without feeling sinful, and I pulled at my thick lisle hose to add conviction.

"Oh, for heaven's sake!" she said scornfully, meaning, either how could I have the vanity to care what my stockings looked like out on a country walk; or else, who in the world was there to see me fix my stocking in this absolutely end-of-the-world place! For once I welcomed that scornful tone. It got in the way of her seeing the truth. And that was all to the good, for me.

I could hardly wait for three twenty, even on a nippy day. I walked towards the end of the line as far as the four corners. Then as we rounded the curve I would start dragging, and gradually everyone passed me. Then, quickly I would dart behind the privet to wait for the girls to round the next curve. After that, it was a matter of a minute to tear across the field and into the graveyard. I had forty-five minutes each day for my work.

My work! I began the very next day to restore the graveyard. I started with my bare hands to tear out the weeds that covered each grave, but the work was very slow, and my nails became torn and my hands cut. So I compounded my sins. I took a tablespoon, a knife, and a fork from the dinner table! They were perfect tools.

Day after day through that early spring, I weeded and pruned. Within ten days the place looked so improved, I could hardly believe I had done it myself. Then I began to straighten some of the stones. Some were too heavy or were completely fallen, but some were just tilted, and I could dig around them and prop them up with small stones and earth.

I knew each stone as if it were a person. Some had blurred old carvings of angels . . . very sweet. Mostly they were just hard-to-read words.

". . . in the thirtieth year of her life . . ." one said, " . . . beloved wife of. . . ." Just fragments were all I could read on some. But one of the later stones, which had not fallen over, had a whole verse on it:

Remember this, as you pass by,
As you are now, so once was I.
As I am now, so you will be.
Prepare to die, and follow me.

That man was the only one in the whole graveyard I did not have a good feeling for, and that may not have been fair. Perhaps he did not choose his own epitaph. Perhaps his mean sister did.

There was one corner I liked best. It was on the far side, away from the gate, where two tall stones had fallen against the fence. They leaned there, wedged into the earth, angled against each other like a strong roof of a house. When the work was well under way, I could take time off just to enjoy the place, and then I would crawl into the "house" and sit, with the sun's rays slanting in, warming me, and the intense quiet of the field and the wonderful new order of the graveyard making me feel quite wonderful.

Spring had really come; I had been working in the graveyard for several weeks, and I was sitting in the "house" one day, writing a sonnet, when I heard a rustling sound. I sat very still and listened. I heard it again, and then I saw a foot. I held my breath until I nearly strangled. I was so terribly frightened, but at the same time, curiously excited.

It was a short, broad foot in a heavy scuffed oxford with big brass eyelets. There were thick gray socks in the shoes, and they reached to the knees, where they met very funny woolen trousers. Suddenly the knees bent, and a face was thrust into my house.

I knew immediately that it was Jimmy Duncan, the president's son. Even though I had never seen him really close before, I recognized his strange build, which was short like a child's, but heavy-set like a man's. The strange thing was that it didn't seem to frighten or startle him that I was there. When he looked into the house, he just smiled at me in a twisted way and acted almost as though he had been expecting to see me. Then he came in and squatted beside me.

I was really quite nervous. The stories about him were so vaguely scary. I kept taking sideways looks at him to see what was so terribly strange about him, but he just sat there not saying a thing. He had his feet pulled up close to him, and he pulled his shoelaces open. Then he started twisting them as if trying to tie them again, but he couldn't

seem to do it. Then he gave that up and took off his woolen cap, which had a snap fastener on it. He spent several minutes snapping and unsnapping it. When he got it snapped, he would smile as though he had done something very fine. All this time, I had been afraid to move, but now I started to relax. I knew it was time to go out to the road and join the other girls. I rose very slowly . . . very slowly. Jimmy didn't move. I said, "Good-by," in a very low voice. Jimmy looked up and smiled.

When the walkers got back to the school, the place was in an uproar. Miss Hill and Dr. Duncan and Jimmy's nurse and the custodian were all looking for him. I never said a word. I couldn't. I felt fairly sure Jimmy wouldn't . . . and couldn't.

I was nervous about going to the graveyard the next day, but I had to go. It was my work. It was an obligation, almost. Jimmy was there before me. He just stood quietly at one corner of the fence and watched me come in and start my work. Once he brought me a small stone. I took it from him and said "Thank you." That's the only thing that was said. He left before I did, without saying good-by.

After that I saw Jimmy in the graveyard many, many times, and I stopped being nervous or afraid. Without his telling me anything, I found out a great many things about him. In the first place, he was very nearly mute. He had a voice, but he never said anything except to make unintelligible sounds now and then. Sometimes he seemed to be talking to himself, though I couldn't understand him, and sometimes he would let out a soft cry. Still, he couldn't have been nearly as stupid as everyone at the school said. If he were, he couldn't have managed to get away from his nurse so often—sometimes without being missed. I thought perhaps this was his rest hour and he just slipped out, or perhaps the nurse was not so alert or spry. Perhaps it was *her* rest hour. Another thing I found out was that the girls were only making it up when they said Jimmy hurt them in any way. He never raised a hand to me except once; but after a while he would hold onto my hand when we sat in the house, and he used to like to stroke the sleeve of my uniform. He would pick up the sleeve and rub it between his fingers. It seemed very comforting to him.

Jimmy didn't come every day, but the third time he came, we started to decorate the graves. We walked about the field, collecting what we could—at first, only early grasses and buds from low bushes. Later, we had buttercups, clover, daisies, and, last of all, Queen Anne's lace. We decorated all the graves and swept them with an old hairbrush, but we kept the children's graves especially beautiful. We put fresh flowers on them every single day and swept and smoothed the earth.

Jimmy loved to pick the flowers, most especially the Queen Anne's lace, but he made odd bouquets because his hands were square and clumsy. The flowers went every which way, even upside down, with the big white lacy heads of Queen Anne hanging down. I laughed and said, "Jimmy, they all have to go this way," and showed him mine, and he would smile. But he became very impatient, and just once really frantic when I tried to fix one of his bouquets that was messy.

After we had tended the graves, we would go and sit together in the house. Sometimes we would just sit and relax, and he would hold onto my hand or my sleeve. But after a while I started to bring books to read to him, and when I did, he would sit absolutely still just staring at me, as if I were some wonderful machine. He loved me to read, but I never really knew how much he understood. I think he liked the poetry best. I read him things I thought he would enjoy for the sound. I read,

"Caliban in the Coal Mine," and "The Highwayman." I read "Abou Ben Adam," and I read him "'Twas Brillig" from *Alice Through the Looking Glass*.

On the days that Jimmy did not come, I was not nearly as content, though I loved the graveyard anyway. On those days that I was alone, I would write poetry, but now I hardly ever wrote of loneliness. I wrote about spring, about the field, about the quiet. After a while, I wrote about love–not being in love, but love, nevertheless–because I knew very clearly then, that except for my family, Jimmy Duncan was the very first person that I ever really loved. I am not sure just how I loved him. I never thought of him as a contemporary. He was ageless. Perhaps he was, as I was, someone unreal–a "transient." But sometimes, as we sat in the house and shared a cracker or a bit of chocolate, I would want to put my arms about his thick shoulders, and pull his poor homely face down to my shoulder, and cradle him. But I never did, and I knew, somehow, that the feeling he had was shown when he ran to meet me, and took my hand, and sat beside me.

There was only one time he upset or frightened me. That day, when we had been sitting in the house for a while, he reached into his pocket and put something down in my lap. It was a mouse. I cried out loudly, and sprang up, and the mouse tumbled off my lap onto the ground. For some reason this terrified Jimmy, and he got a really tortured and terrible look on his face that made me think he was going to scream, too, and that is when he looked as though he would strike out at me. But all he did was whimper, and then I said quite calmly, "Jimmy, please take it out of the house." The mouse had just been sitting there the whole time. I suppose it was half suffocated, and the tumble didn't help. Jimmy picked it up and took it out to the gate and put it down. Then he gave it a push and it ran a little way into the grass. I didn't know if he had meant it for a present, or if he had just wanted to bring it to our field.

In his own way, I felt that Jimmy loved me, too. The warming effect of this feeling touched me slowly but strongly. As we worked together, as we sat in the house, reading, day after day, I sometimes had the sense of standing apart and above the scene. I could look down and see someone in the house that was a *real* person, and that person started to take on the shape of me—me next to another person, Jimmy—a good positive place, an important place. For the first time in my whole life, I began to have a sense of myself, and I didn't care if no one at school seemed to notice the change. It was enough to gradually feel myself grow strong.

And then, for a whole week, Jimmy didn't come. At first I didn't worry. He had often been away a few days in a row. But when he hadn't come by the second week, my only thought was, "He's been found out. They found out how he did it. He won't be able to come anymore." But I really felt he would find a way.

I didn't see him at all about the school, even in the distance, as I had usually seen him, walking with his nurse. By the end of the third week I was terribly, terribly lonely and very worried. I missed him. I missed him very much.

And then, in chapel one lovely morning near the end of the term, with the late June sunshine making even that dreadful room a beautiful place, Miss Hill announced "Dr. Duncan's son James died last night after a long and disabling illness." A special memorial service was to be held.

I, who could cry for myself at night, who could cry for six children, dead more than a hundred years, did not cry for Jimmy Duncan, but I had a terrible, terrible pain in my throat for days, and my eyes hurt as though I had been struck hard.

They buried him somewhere out of the state. I could not even put flowers on his grave.

Perversely, then, in all the quiet drear of Mary Barrows, something did happen, but it was not in a way that anyone could have foreseen, so they may have no credit for it— not my parents, nor The Mary Barrows School. All in a few months, I had come to see myself as a real person in the real world, and had loved and been loved, been bereaved, and had grown, with great pain and pride, in a sunny field of buttercups, and Queen Anne's lace, and dead children.